This edition published by Parragon Books Ltd in 2016

Parragon Books Ltd
Chartist House
15–17 Trim Street
Bath BA1 1HA, UK
www.parragon.com

Chase's Space Case: By Kristen L. Depken. Illustrated by MJ Illustrations.

Pups Save the Bunnies: Based on the teleplay "Pups Save the Bunnies"
by Ursula Ziegler Sullivan. Illustrated by MJ Illustrations.

Rubble to the Rescue: By Kristen L. Depken. Illustrated by MJ Illustrations.

Ice Team: Based on the episode "The New Pup" by Ursula Ziegler-Sullivan.
Illustrated by MJ Illustrations.

ISBN 978-1-4748-4297-6

T#492478

Printed in China

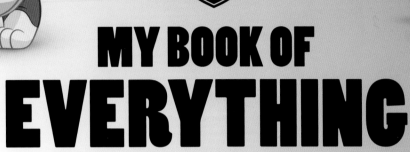

MY BOOK OF
EVERYTHING

Story: Chase's Space Case 7

Story: Pups Save the Bunnies 31

PAWsome Activities 49

Story: Rubble to the Rescue 179

Story: Ice Team 203

PaRragon

Bath · New York · Cologne · Melbourne · Delhi
Hong Kong · Shenzhen · Singapore

PAW Patrol

Chase's Space Case

One night, Ryder, Skye and Rocky were looking at the stars. Suddenly they thought they saw one falling.

Ryder grabbed his binoculars to get a closer look. "That doesn't look like a star to me," he said. "It looks like some kind of spaceship."

"Cool!" said Skye. "I wonder if we'll see any aliens."

But Ryder looked worried. "It's heading right for Adventure Bay!"

The spaceship flew through the sky and crash-landed
on Farmer Yumi's farm.

As it hit the ground, a beam of light shot out and
trapped Bettina the cow in a space bubble.

Someone must have been flying the spaceship,
but there was no sign of any aliens….

Ryder got a call from Mayor Goodway. She was just leaving Farmer Yumi's house when she spotted the cow floating in the bubble.

"Can you help poor Bettina and find out what is going on here?" Mayor Goodway asked.

"We're on it, Mayor Goodway," replied Ryder. "No job is too big, no pup is too small!"

Ryder called the pups to the Lookout. For this mission, he needed Rocky's recycling skills to fix the spaceship and Chase's detective skills to find the pilot.

The team jumped in their trucks and rushed over to Farmer Yumi's farm.

At the farm, Chase used the net in his Pup Pack
to pop the bubble and save Bettina the cow.

Then Chase started to look for clues, hoping they would help him find the pilot of the spaceship.

Searching through the cornfields, Chase found some strange footprints in the mud. He began to follow them....

Chase didn't find the pilot but he did find
Mayor Goodway … floating in a bubble!
    "Mayor Goodway?" Chase began, confused.
"How did you get up there?"
    "A little green alien beamed me up," she replied.

Chase was shocked. "A real alien! I've got to see this."
He began to run off when Mayor Goodway stopped him.
"Still floating in an alien bubble up here!" she shouted.
"Oops," said Chase. "Sorry, Mayor."
Chase barked to activate his Pup Pack. Out shot his net,
which burst the Mayor's bubble and she landed on the ground.

After helping Mayor Goodway, Chase continued his search.

Suddenly, he thought he'd found something. "A round, green head!" Chase gasped. But when he looked closer he realized it was just a melon.

He began walking past the row of green fruit. "Melon, melon, alien, melon...." Chase stopped in his tracks. "Alien!"

The alien tried to speak, but Chase couldn't understand what he was saying. Then the alien got scared and trapped Chase in a space bubble!

Chase started to bark for help, but then realized he could use his net to save himself – just as he'd done for the cow and Mayor Goodway.

Once he was free, Chase ran to find Ryder and the other pups. He needed to tell them all about the alien.

Back at the Lookout, Ryder and the PAW Patrol were
suddenly greeted by an unexpected guest ... the alien!
He thought the Lookout was another spaceship, so he was
trying to fly it home.

"Sorry, buddy," Ryder told him. "That's not going to work."

The alien was very upset. He missed his mum and wanted to go home.

Ryder called Rocky on his PupPad. "Rocky, have you fixed the spaceship yet? We've got a stranded alien here."

"Look out of the window...." Rocky replied.

Ryder and the pups looked outside and saw Rocky floating in mid-air, flying the alien's spaceship!
The alien jumped with joy when he saw his spaceship had been fixed. He smiled at Ryder and the pups.

"Whenever you're in trouble, just yelp for help!"
said Ryder, and they all rushed outside to see
the spaceship.

SKYE

To thank Ryder and the PAW Patrol for all their help, the alien gave everyone a ride.

"We're flying in a spaceship," said Skye, as they zoomed past Mayor Goodway. "How cool is that?"

Soon, it was time for the alien to go home. He dropped Ryder and the pups back at the Lookout and then flew off into space.

"Coolest. Ride. Ever!" cheered Ryder, as he and the pups waved goodbye to their new alien friend.

The End

Pups Save the Bunnies

It was a sunny day and Mr Porter was visiting Farmer Yumi to get some carrots for his market. But there was a problem … the carrots were disappearing into the dirt!

"These carrots are growing backwards!" Mr Porter cried.
But Farmer Yumi knew what was really happening – bunnies
were eating her carrots.
This was a job for the PAW Patrol!

After Ryder had received the call from Farmer Yumi, he
gathered the PAW Patrol in the Lookout, and told them about
the bunnies.

"We need to move them to a field where they'll be safe and
won't eat Farmer Yumi's carrots," Ryder said. "Rubble, I'll need
your shovel so we can find the bunnies' tunnels."

"Rubble on the double!" he yelped.

"And Chase, I'll need your megaphone and herding skills to round up the bunnies," Ryder continued.

"Chase is on the case!" the police pup barked.

Ryder, Rubble and Chase raced to Farmer Yumi's farm.
"Let's dig in!" Rubble said, and he lowered his shovel
into the ground, in search of the bunny tunnels. "I think
I've found something!" he shouted a few moments later.
"In fact, I've found two somethings!"

Ryder needed a way to carry the two bunnies from the farm.

He called Rocky and Skye on his PupPad. "Rocky, can you get some old kennel cages so Skye can fly them here?"

"Don't lose it – reuse it!" Rocky said.

"And I'll be there in two shakes of a bunny's tail," Skye added.

Soon, Skye arrived with the kennel cages and
Chase started herding the bunnies into them.

"Attention, all bunnies!" Chase announced through his megaphone. "We've brought cages with nice, soft beds to take you to your new homes."

"And inside each cage," Skye added, "is a crunchy treat."

The bunnies hopped into the cages and Skye carried them to their new field in her helicopter.

But the busy day wasn't over yet. When Mr Porter returned
to his market he found some furry-tailed surprises in the box
of vegetables he'd brought from the farm.
This was another job for the PAW Patrol!

The team hurried off to Mr Porter's market.
"I need some of your delicious carrot cake, Mr Porter,"
Ryder said. He had a plan for how to catch the bunnies.

Ryder set the cake on the ground and all the bunnies bounded over to it. "Now we need your net, Chase!"
Chase launched his net over the bunnies and Ryder carefully scooped them up inside.

Skye carried the last of the bunnies to their new home in the faraway field. As soon as Ryder opened the kennel cages, the little bunnies bounced into the grass and began to munch happily on flowers.

"Bye-bye, bunnies," Skye said. "I'm going to miss you."

When Skye returned to the Lookout, she realized she wasn't alone – a bunny had stowed away inside her helicopter!

"Can we keep her?" Skye asked.

"I think we can handle one bunny," Ryder said.

"Ryder, you're the best," Skye cheered as the pups welcomed their new furry friend.

The End

PAWsome Activities

When there's trouble in Adventure Bay,
PAW Patrol is ready for action!

"I'm ready to fight blazes,"
says Marshall the brave fire pup.

"I'm always on patrol!" yells Chase the police dog.

"My shovel often comes in handy,"
barks Rubble the construction pup.

"I love the view of Adventure Bay from up in my helicopter!" cries Skye the fearless pilot pup.

"I can find a use for anything," barks Rocky,
PAW Patrol's top recycler.

"I like to make a splash!" says Zuma,
the water-loving labrador.

Ryder is the PAW Patrol leader. He and the pups
are always ready to save the day.

The PAW Patrol love to visit Katie
at the Pup Parlour.

Katie's cat Cali is the purr-fect pet.

Chase can race to the rescue
in his PAWsome police truck.

Whenever someone's in trouble, Marshall jumps in his fire truck to save the day.

Rocky's recycling truck is the perfect vehicle
to help him move other people's rubbish.

Rubble has a big digger that
comes with a drill and a shovel.

Skye can fly over Adventure Bay in her helicopter
and keep an eye out for anyone in trouble.

Zuma zooms over the water in his hovercraft,
ready to reach an emergency on the water.

Ryder drives a hi-tech ATV. It can turn
into a jet ski or a snowmobile, too!

Draw lines to connect the food bowls to the correct pups.

1

2

3

4

5

6

a

b

c

d

e

f

The pups deserve a treat.
How many dog biscuits can you count?

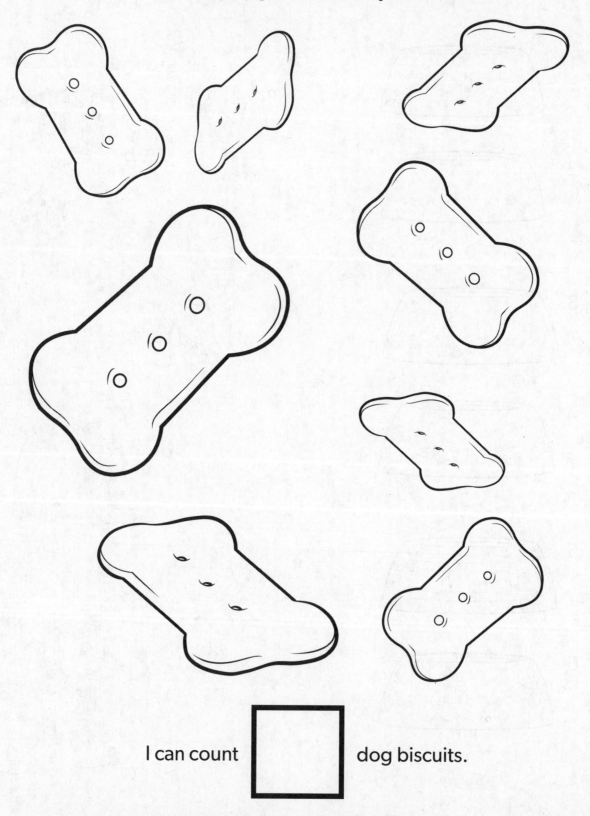

I can count [ ] dog biscuits.

ANSWER: 8 dog biscuits

Look at these two pictures of Ryder's PupPad.
Can you circle five differences in the bottom picture?

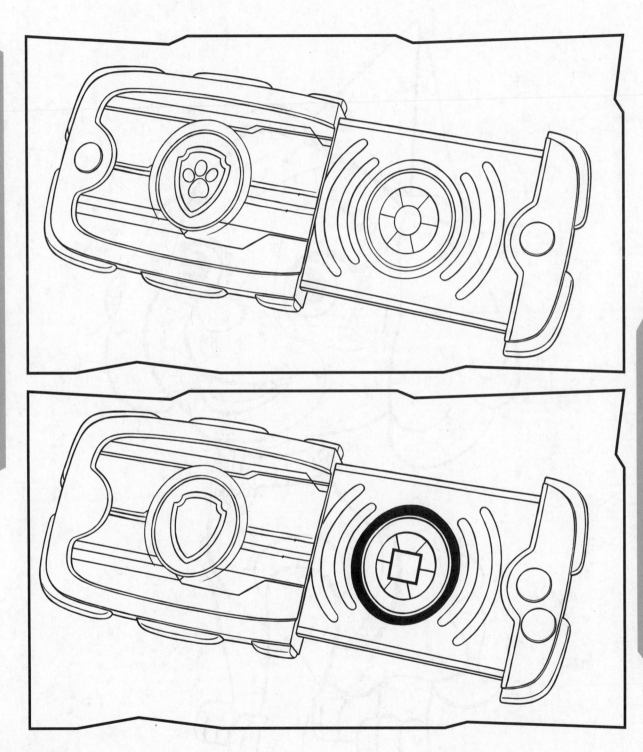

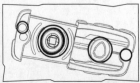

ANSWER:

It's Halloween and the PAW Patrol are having a party!
Skye is a PAWsome princess.

Ryder is dressed as a brave knight.

Zuma loves the water, so a pirate
costume is the perfect choice for him.

Rubble is ready to sing like a famous
pop star for some trick-or-treat sweets.

Marshall is dressed as a pumpkin. He likes the
colour orange almost as much as red!

Katie and Cali have joined the pups' party.
Their costumes are spook-tastic!

Rocky looks totally PAWsome in his costume.

Chase is bobbing for apples.
How many apples can you count?

I can count [ ] apples.

Captain Zuma is sailing across the high seas.

Oops! Careful, Marshall!

Spot and circle the spooky Halloween-themed objects.

ANSWER:

The PAW Patrol are having so much fun.
They all love Halloween and dressing up!

Today, Marshall is in training to run Adventure Bay's Fire Rescue Course.

The PAW Patrol cheer on their friend!

Marshall runs and jumps and – oops! He trips.

Now Marshall is on a roll!
He easily jumps through the tyres.

"Here I come, Cali!" calls Marshall.
"Ladder up and – oh no!"
Marshall's cat rescue isn't going to plan ...

... and he falls off the ladder.
"I'm not going to break any fire pup records
today," says Marshall. "All I'm good
at breaking are ladders."

"It looks like Marshall could use a helping hand,"
says Ryder. "PAW Patrol to the Lookout!"

"We have an emergency," says Ryder.
"And that emergency is Marshall.
He needs our help!"

"Marshall, we just want you to try your best and not worry about breaking the record."

"Rocky, I need you to find something to fix Marshall's ladder," says Ryder.

"Marshall, I need you and your fire gear ready to do your best."

"I'll try to do my best … and forget about the rest."

"I can use this broom handle to make rungs for Marshall's ladder," says Rocky.

"Good work, Rocky," says Ryder.

On the day of the race, Chase gets ready
to take Marshall to the starting point.

"My cones will stop the traffic until
Marshall gets here," says Chase.

"Good morning, Adventure Bay!"
says Mayor Goodway.

"Today Marshall will attempt the fastest
Fire Rescue Course run ever!"

"Do my best and forget the rest," says Marshall.

Ready! Set! Go!

Marshall almost trips during the tyre obstacle challenge. "I'm okay," he says.

Marshall finishes the animal rescue without a problem!

"He's making really good time,"
says Ryder. "Go, Marshall!"

Marshall shoots water from his fire hose and hits the target!

"Now I just have to get to the finish line!" says Marshall.

Uh-oh! The cameraman accidentally knocks over a light and starts a fire.

107

Marshall stops to
put out the fire.

108

Marshall runs as fast as he can to finish the race....

Oh no! Marshall didn't get the record.

"That's okay," Marshall says. "I did my best."

"Because you stopped to put out a real fire, you're an Adventure Bay Hero," the mayor says.

Hooray for Marshall, the greatest fire pup in the world!

Circle the picture of Marshall that is different from the others.

a

b

c

d

Marshall is looking through the big telescope. He hopes that a flock of geese will return to Adventure Bay soon.

Do you see a goose? Circle it.

ANSWER:

Rocky builds a nest for tired geese and then Rubble fills the nest with bread.

"Looks like the geese are here," says Ryder.

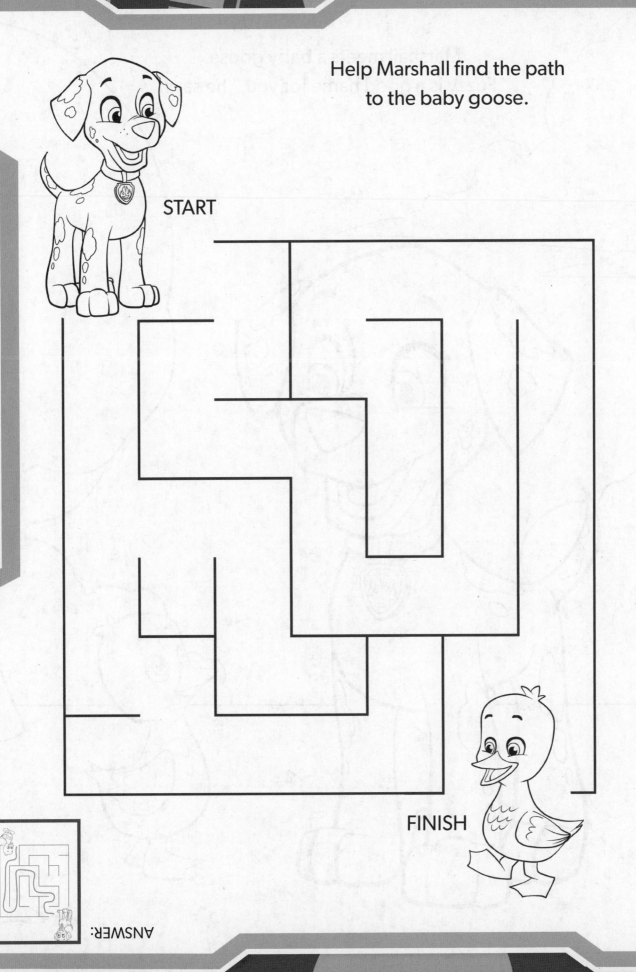

Help Marshall find the path to the baby goose.

START

FINISH

ANSWER:

119

Marshall meets a baby goose.
"Fuzzy is a good name for you," he says.

"Looks like you have a new BGFF –
Best Goose Friend Forever," says Skye.

Draw a picture of your best friend.

Marshall washes his fire truck.

Fuzzy dries the windows.

Marshall makes sure that Fuzzy
gets enough to eat.

Marshall trips on his food bowl
and Fuzzy does, too!

Fuzzy wants Marshall to sleep
outside with the geese.

Good night, Fuzzy.

Fuzzy wakes up before Marshall and wanders
off to eat breadcrumbs.

"Fuzzy is gone!" says Marshall. "We have to find him before his flock leaves."

"PAW Patrol, to the Lookout!"

Zuma and Skye get Ryder's alert
and their dog tags light up.

Rubble and Rocky come running.

Draw lines to connect the badges
to the correct pups.

1

a

2

b

3

c

4

d

ANSWER: 1–b, 2–c, 3–d, 4–a

Draw a big fire hat for Marshall.

"I'm all fired up!"

"Skye! This pup's gotta fly!"

"Rocky to the rescue!"

"Rubble on the double!"

"Let's dive in!"

PAW Patrol is at the Lookout.

"PAW Patrol, ready for action, Ryder, sir!" says Chase.

"Marshall's friend Fuzzy is missing," says Ryder.
"We have to find him!"

"Chase, we'll need your megaphone to call Fuzzy," says Ryder.

Marshall will help look, too.

Draw lines to connect each pup to their truck.

1

a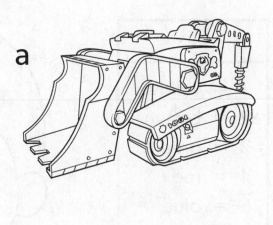

2

b

3

c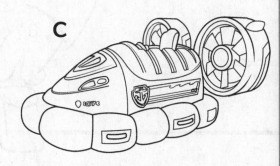

4

d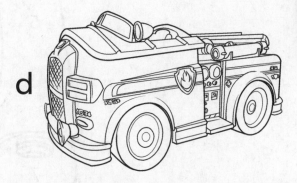

PAW Patrol is on a roll!
Use the key to colour in the picture.

KEY

1 = yellow
2 = brown
3 = green
4 = red
5 = blue
6 = pink
7 = grey

The search begins!

Chase calls for Fuzzy. "Honk! Honk!"

Be a police pup and figure out which picture
of Chase is different from the others. Circle it!

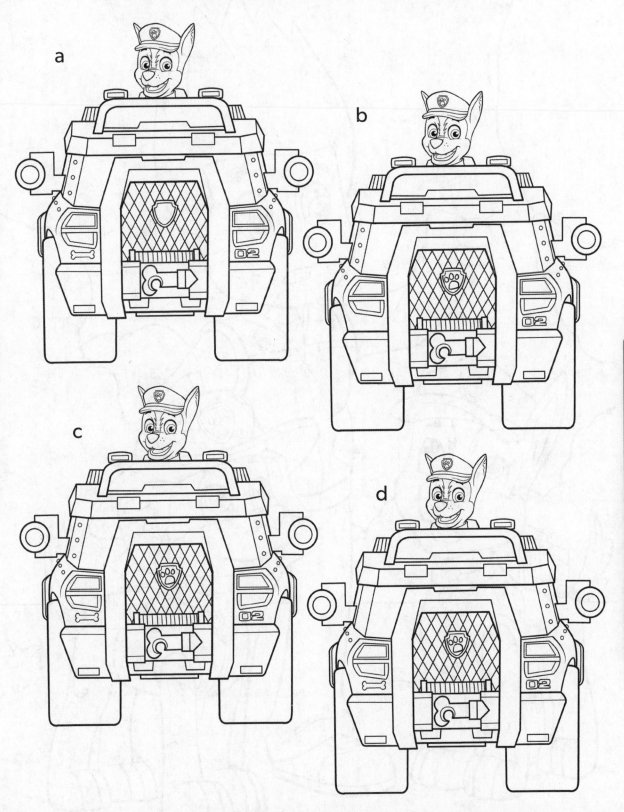

a

b

c

d

151

Marshall finds one of Fuzzy's feathers. Chase gives it a sniff.

"Achoo! I'm a little allergic to feathers," says Chase.

Chase is on the case!
Use the key to colour in the picture.

KEY

1	=	blue
2	=	yellow
3	=	brown
4	=	red
5	=	black

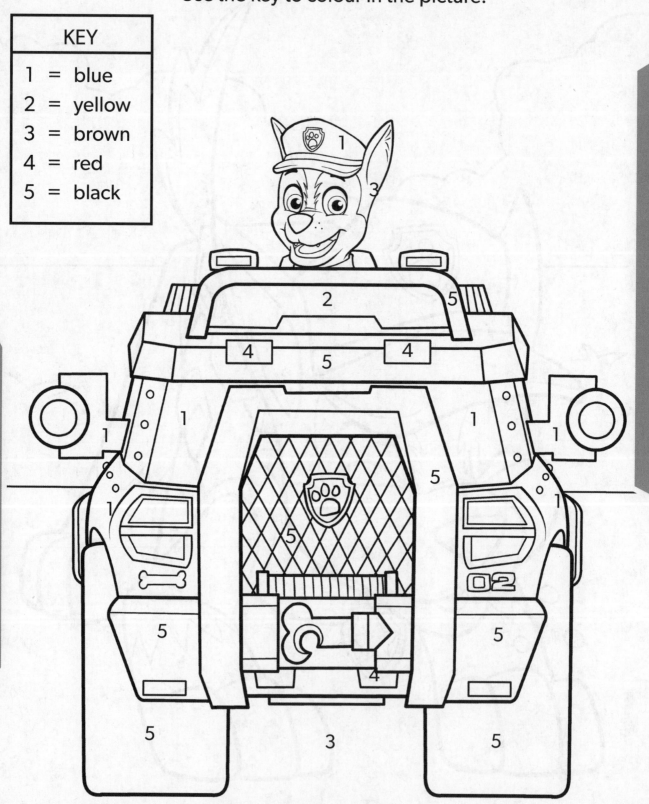

Help Marshall find Fuzzy!

START

FINISH

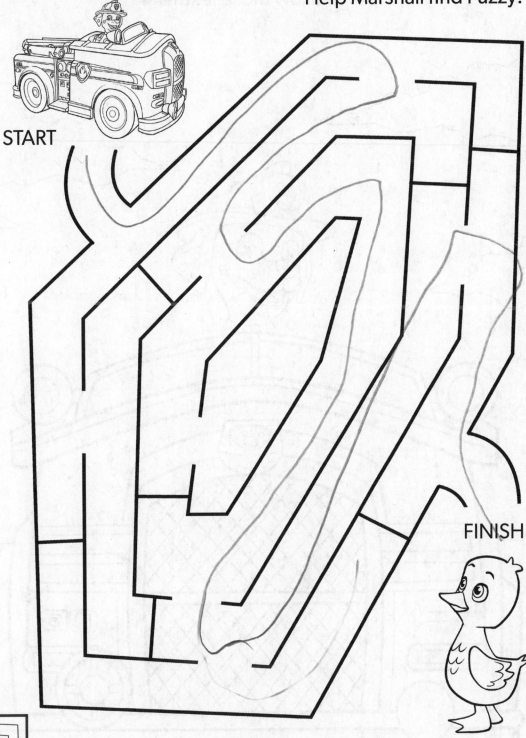

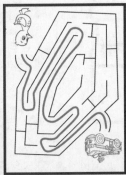

ANSWER:

155

Oh no! Those seagulls are picking on Fuzzy and he can't fly away because he's trapped in a plastic ring.

Chase's net takes care of the seagulls.

"Marshall, use your ladder to climb up to Fuzzy," says Ryder.

Marshall rescues Fuzzy.

"Great job!"

Chase and Marshall are a terrific team!

"The geese are flying away!" cries Ryder.
"Fuzzy has to catch up with them."

Fuzzy doesn't want to leave Marshall.

"If Fuzzy doesn't leave now, he'll never catch up with the other geese," says Ryder. "Wait, I have an idea!"

Ryder puts a special flying vest on Marshall.

The vest is tied to Skye's helicopter and then Skye takes off!

KEY	
1 =	pink
2 =	brown
3 =	tan
4 =	silver
5 =	blue

Marshall is flying! Fuzzy is following him.

Marshall and Fuzzy catch up
with the geese.

Draw Fuzzy flying with his friends.

"Bye, Fuzzy, you silly goose!"

"You pups did a really great job today," says Ryder.

"Hooray for the PAW Patrol!" barks Rocky.

Rocky to the rescue!
Use the key to colour in the picture.

KEY

1 = yellow
2 = orange
3 = green
4 = grey
5 = blue

Look at the top picture of the PAW Patrol.
Can you circle five differences in the bottom picture?

ANSWER:

Whenever there's trouble, just yelp for help!

Rubble to
the Rescue

The PAW Patrol pups loved to watch their favourite hero, Apollo the Super Pup, save the day in his own super way.

"Wow!" Rubble said when the show ended. "Isn't Apollo the super-est Super Pup ever?"

Just then, Ryder walked in and invited the pups to play football outside. "Coming, Rubble?" asked Ryder.

"No thanks," Rubble replied. "I'm going to play Rubble the Super Pup and save the day, my own way."

"Hmm ... who can I save?" Rubble asked Ryder.

"Farmer Yumi might need help around the farm," Ryder suggested.

"Great idea, Ryder," shouted Rubble, as he headed straight out of the door.

"Hi, Farmer Yumi," Rubble called as he arrived at the farm. "Need a Super Pup to save the day?"

"My chickens flew the coop when I left the door open," she explained. "Can you help, Super Pup?"

"Don't worry," announced Rubble. "Here comes Rubble the Super Pup to save the day!"

Rubble ran at a group of chickens, and they leaped into the air in surprise! Then he steered the startled chickens back into their coop.

"Is there anything else Rubble the Super Pup can do for you?" he asked Farmer Yumi.

"I've done my chores," she replied. "But Mayor Goodway might need some help."

"Rubble the Super Pup is here to save the day!"
Rubble said as he arrived at City Hall.
Mayor Goodway dashed past him looking worried.
"Hi, Mayor Goodway," Rubble called.

"You're just the pup I need," she said. "There's been a rockslide and the train is stuck inside Mountain Tunnel."

"Don't worry, Mayor Goodway," Rubble assured her. "Rubble the Super Pup is here to save the day!"

Rubble decided he didn't need to stop Ryder and the pups' football game – he could save the day, his own way!

"There you are, Rubble," said the train engineer when Rubble arrived at the tunnel. "I knew the PAW Patrol would save the day! But where is Ryder and the other pups?"

"We don't need Ryder and the PAW Patrol," said Rubble. "Rubble the Super Pup can handle this. Just like Apollo the Super Pup does – all on my own!"

The engineer wasn't so sure. He was worried that more rocks could fall down if Rubble wasn't careful. But the Super Pup was confident that he could save the day.

Rubble charged at the fallen rocks, but they wouldn't budge. He charged again, this time pushing a boulder out from underneath the rockslide.

"Look out!" shouted the engineer as more rocks fell down, blocking the entrance completely.

"Quick! We have to get out the other side," said Rubble.

But as they raced towards the other end of the
tunnel, more rocks fell down and blocked the exit!
"I'm sorry," Rubble said, sinking to the floor.
"I thought I could do it myself, but I've just made
everything worse."

Rubble sat up. He knew exactly what to do – yelp for help! The tag around Rubble's neck lit up as he called Ryder and the PAW Patrol.

"Hi, Ryder," said Rubble. "I need the PAW Patrol on the double. There was a rockslide at Mountain Tunnel and now we're trapped!"

"Don't worry, Rubble," Ryder said. "No job is too big, no pup is too small! We're on our way."
Using his PupPad, Ryder gathered the rest of the PAW Patrol and set off to rescue Rubble. The PAW Patrol was on a roll!

The PAW Patrol arrived at Mountain Tunnel, ready for action. "Chase is on the case!" Chase said. He used the winch on his police truck to move some of the rocks and create an exit. Rubble squeezed through the gap. "Thanks, Chase," he said. "Now, how can I help?"

"Okay, Rubble," said Ryder, giving Rubble a big thumbs up. "You know what to do."

Rubble drove his digger towards the rockslide. He scooped up the rocks blocking the tunnel and moved them safely away.

When all the rocks had been moved, the engineer drove
the train out of the tunnel. "Rubble, you did it!" he cheered.
"You saved the day – your own way!"

Rubble shook his head and smiled at Chase and Zuma.
"You mean I helped save the day – the PAW Patrol way."

As the train pulled away, the engineer tooted the horn in thanks. Ryder gave each of the pups a pat on the head to congratulate them on saving the day. "Now let's go and play together," said Rubble. "The PAW Patrol way!"

The End

Ice Team

One sunny day, the PAW Patrol was getting ready for a trip to see their friend Jake at the ice fields.

Suddenly, there was a loud roar, and a big truck rolled up.

"Presenting the PAW Patroller!" Ryder announced. "It's a Lookout on wheels. It can take us anywhere. And Robo Dog will be our driver!"

A door opened in the side and a mechanical dog hopped out.

As Ryder was showing the pups around the PAW Patroller, Jake called.

"Hey, Jake! How are the ice fields?" Ryder asked.

"Amazing!" Jake declared. "Take a look!" The screen showed snowy hills and an icy river.

Just then, Jake slipped on the ice and the pups could hear him yell, "My phone! My maps! All my stuff!" Jake's equipment had splashed into the icy river!

"Jake's in big trouble!" Rubble exclaimed.

"Pups, get your vehicles," Ryder said.

The PAW Patroller's back door opened and a ramp came out. The pups quickly drove their vehicles aboard. Robo Dog started the engine and the PAW Patroller rolled into action.

At the ice fields, Jake was trying to get his backpack out of the water. But the riverbank was so icy that he began to slide in! Luckily, a husky pup pulled him out.

"Sweet save!" Jake said, then he introduced himself.

"I'm Everest," the pup replied. "I rescued someone! I've always wanted to do a real rescue."

"We should probably get going," Everest said.
"A storm's rolling in. I wouldn't want to lose my first
real rescue in a blizzard. We can wait it out in my igloo.
To get there, we can do this...."

Everest flopped onto her belly and slid down the hill.
"Belly-bogganing!" Jake shouted, taking off after her.
"Look out below!"
The two new friends slid along on the ice, zooming past some penguins.

When the PAW Patroller reached the ice fields, the snow was falling hard. The team started to look for Jake. They quickly found his frozen phone and pack.

"This means Jake doesn't have any supplies," Ryder said. Then he noticed something in the snow. "Are those tracks?"

Chase gave the tracks a sniff. "That's Jake, all right! And he's got another pup with him."

"Those tracks should lead us to Jake," Ryder said. "Let's follow them."

As Chase followed the tracks on the ground,
Skye took to the frosty air. "This pup's got to fly!"

Everest and Jake came to a narrow bridge that stretched across a deep, dark ravine. "My igloo is just across that ice bridge," Everest said.

"Will it hold us?" Jake asked.

"I hope so," the husky replied. "It's the only way to get over."

As they walked across, they heard a terrible cracking noise. The ice bridge was breaking!

Just as the bridge collapsed, Skye swooped in, catching Jake and Everest with a rope. But before she had carried them to the other side of the ravine, the rope broke.

"Jump!" Jake yelled to Everest.

Everest landed on a ledge, but Jake missed it.
He caught the edge with his fingers and dangled
dangerously over the dark ravine.

"Don't worry!" Everest yelled. "I've got you!"
She snagged Jake's sleeve and pulled him to safety.
"Yes – two rescues in one day!"

Everyone went to Jake's cabin on the mountain for roasted marshmallows – and a surprise.

"Everest," Jake said, "I could use a smart pup like you to help out on the mountain."

"And for saving Jake and showing great rescue skills," Ryder added, "I'd like to make you an official member of the PAW Patrol!"

"This is the best day ever!" Everest cried, and all the pups cheered.

The End